The
PETER RABBIT™
Birthday Book

FREDERICK WARNE
Published by the Penguin Group
Penguin Books Ltd, 80 Strand, London WC2R 0RL, England
Penguin Putnam Inc., 375 Hudson Street, New York, New York 10014, USA
Penguin Books Australia Ltd, 250 Camberwell Road, Camberwell, Victoria 3124, Australia
Penguin Books Canada Ltd, 10 Alcorn Avenue, Toronto, Ontario, Canada M4V 3B2
Penguin Books India (P) Ltd, 11 Community Centre, Panchsheel Park, New Delhi 110 017, India
Penguin Books (NZ) Ltd, Cnr Rosedale and Airborne Roads, Albany, Auckland, New Zealand
Penguin Books (South Africa) (Pty) Ltd, P O Box 9, Parklands 2121, South Africa
Penguin Books Ltd, Registered Offices: 80 Strand, London WC2R 0RL, England
Web site at: www.peterrabbit.com

This edition published in 2003
First published by Frederick Warne in 1999
Copyright © Frederick Warne & Co., 1999
New reproductions of Beatrix Potter's book illustrations copyright © Frederick Warne & Co., 2002
Original illustrations copyright © Frederick Warne & Co., 1902, 1903, 1904,
1905, 1906, 1907, 1908, 1909, 1910, 1911, 1912,
1913, 1917, 1918, 1922, 1930, 1955, 1971
Frederick Warne & Co. is the owner of all rights, copyrights and trademarks in the
Beatrix Potter character names and illustrations.

ISBN 0 7232 4539 8
Printed in China

The PETER RABBIT™
Birthday Book

FREDERICK WARNE

The pie proved extremely toothsome, and the muffins light and hot. They disappeared rapidly, especially the pie!

January

January 1

January 2

January 3

January 4

January 5

January 6

January

January 7

January 8

January 9

January 10

January 11

Kelly George B.D.

January 12

They got amongst flowerpots, and frames and
tubs; Peter heard noises worse than ever, his eyes
were as big as lolly-pops!

January

January 13

January 14

January 15

Barb's Birthday

January 16

January 17

January 18

January

January 19

January 20

January 21

January 22

January 23

January 24

_____

_____

January 25

_____

_____

January

January 26

January 27

January 28

January 29

January 30

January 31

February

February 1

February 2

February 3

February 4

February 5

February 6

February

February 7

February 8

February 9

February 10

February 11

February 12

February

February 13

February 14

February 15

Susans B.D.

February 16

February 17

February 18

Mom's B.D.

The little person made a bob-curtsey—"Oh, yes, if you please'm; my name is Mrs. Tiggy-winkle; oh, yes if you please'm, I'm an excellent clear-starcher!"

February

February 19

February 20

February 21

February 22

February 23

February 24

February

February 25

Kathy Ford   B.D.

February 26

February 27

February 28

February 29

March

March 1

March 2

March 3

March 4

March 5

March 6

"I am sure you will never want to live in
town again," said Timmy Willie.

March

March 7

March 8

March 9

March 10

Kokos b.d.

March 11

March 12

March

March 13

March 14

March 15

March 16

March 17

Sandi + Damas b.d.

March 18

March 19

_____

_____

March

March 20

Roy's B.D.

March 21

March 22

March 23

March 24

March 25

March

March 26

March 27

March 28

March 29

March 30

March 31

April

April 1

April 2

April 3

April 4

April 5

April

April 6

April 7

April 8

April 9

April 10

April 11

"A minnow! A minnow! I have him by the nose!"
cried Mr. Jeremy Fisher, jerking up his rod.

April

April 12

April 13

April 14

Karls b.d.   Royk bday

April 15

Terry's b.d.

April 16

April 17

April

April 18

April 19

April 20

Emily's B.D. 94

April 21

April 22

April 23

April 24

April

April 25

April 26

April 27

Shawna's b.d.

April 28

April 29

April 30

May

May 1

May 2

May 3

May 4

May 5

May 6

May

May 7

May 8

May 9

May 10

May 11

May

May 12

May 13

May 14

May 15

May 16

May 17

Donna's B.D.

When the three kittens were ready, Mrs. Tabitha unwisely turned them out into the garden, to be out of the way while she made hot buttered toast.

May

May 18

May 19

May 20

May 21

May 22

May 23

May

May 24

May 25

May 26

May 27

May 28

May 29

May 30

_____

_____

May 31

_____

_____

June

June 1

June 2

June 3

June 4

June 5

June 6

June

June 7

_____

_____

June 8

_____

_____

June 9

_____

_____

June 10

_____

_____

June 11

_____

_____

June 12

_____

_____

June

June 13

June 14

June 15

June 16

June 17

Jodis bd.

June 18

June

June 19

June 20

June 21

June 22

June 23

June 24

Jemima Puddle-duck went up the cart road for
the last time, on a sunny afternoon. She was
rather burdened with bunches of herbs and two
onions in a bag.

June

June 25

June 26

June 27

June 28

June 29

June 30

July

July 1

July 2

July 3

July 4

July 5

July 6

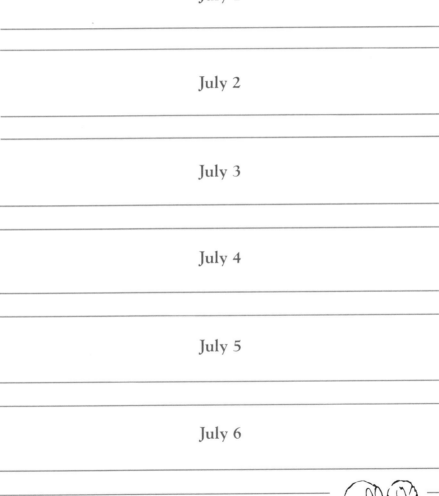

July

July 7

July 8

July 9

July 10

July 11

July 12

As there was not always quite enough to eat—
Benjamin used to borrow cabbages from Flopsy's
brother, Peter Rabbit, who kept a nursery garden.

July

July 13

July 14

July 15

July 16

July 17

July 18

July

July 19

Haley's B.D. 95 Krystals

July 20

July 21

July 22

July 23

July 24

July 25

Lisa's b.d.

July

July 26

July 27

July 28

July 29

July 30

July 31

August

August 1

August 2

August 3

August 4

August 5

August 6

August

August 7

August 8

August 9

August

August 10

August 11

August 12

August 13

August 14

August 15

And because the Mouse has teased Miss Moppet—
Miss Moppet thinks she will tease the mouse;
which is not at all nice of Miss Moppet.

August

August 16

August 17

August 18

August 19

August 20

August 21

August

August 22

August 23

Augus 24

August 25

August 26

August 27

August

August 28

August 29

August 30

August 31

"Tiddly, widdly, widdly! Pouff, pouff, puff!" said Mr. Jackson. He blew the thistle-down all over the room.

September

September 1

September 2

September 3

September 4

September 5

September 6

September

September 7

September 8

September 9

September 10

September 11

September 12

September

September 13

September 14

September 15

Darryls B.D.

September 16

Connies / Arinàs B.D.

September 17

September 18

His mother was busy cooking; she wondered what he had done with his clothes. It was the second little jacket and pair of shoes that Peter had lost in a fortnight!

September

September 19

September 20

September 21

September 22

September 23

September 24

September

September 25

September 26

September 27

September 28

September 29

September 30

October

October 1

October 2

October 3

October 4

October 5

October 6

The other squirrels hunted up and down the
nut bushes; but Nutkin gathered robin's
pin-cushions off a briar bush, and stuck them
full of pine-needle pins.

October 7

October 8

October 9

October 10

October

October 11

October 12

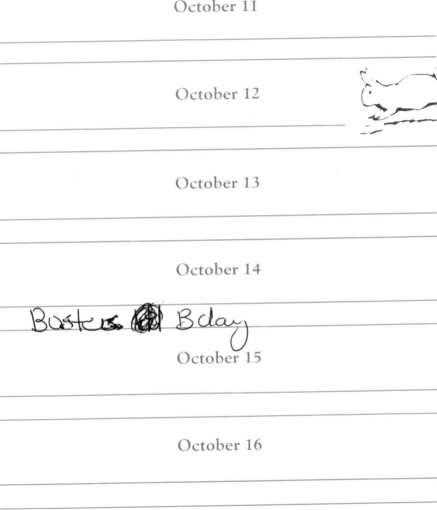

October 13

October 14

Busters 🔵 Bday

October 15

October 16

October

October 17

Andrews bd

October 18

October 19

October 20

October 21

October 22

My BDay

October 23

_____

_____

October 24

_____

_____

October 25

_____

_____

October

October 26

October 27

October 28

October 29

October 30

October 31

November

November 1

November 2

November 3

November

November 4

November 5

November 6

November 7

November 8

November 9

Barrys bday

November

November 10

November 11

November 12

November 13

November 14

November

November 15

Robyns b.day.

November 16

November 17

November 18

November 19

November 20

November

November 21

November 22

November 23

November 24

November 25

November 26

"Why on earth don't you run away?" exclaimed the horrified Pigling.

"I shall after supper," said Pig-wig decidedly.

November

November 27

November 28

November 29

November 30

December

December 1

December 2

December 3

December 4

December 5

December 6

December

December 7

December 8

December

December 9

December 10

December 11

December 12

December 13

December 14

She found some tiny canisters upon the
dresser, labelled—Rice—Coffee—Sago—
but when she turned them upside down,
there was nothing inside except red and
blue beads.

December 15

December 16

December 17

December 18

December 19

Amandas B. Day

December

December 20

December 21

December 22

December 23

December 24

December 25

And when she peeps out
there is nobody there,
But a present of carrots
put down on the stair.

December

December 26

December 27

December 28

December 29

December 30

December 31